First Edition Published by IngramSpark -
2021

First paperback edition July 2021

ISBN 978-1-7776949-8-2 Hardcover
ISBN 978-1-7776949-7-5 Paperback
ISBN 978-1-7776949-6-8 EBook

Published by A Bird House Press

Mitch: Thanks for insisting that I sit at the stern on our first canoe trip together! I can't imagine what would have happened, if you had let me have my way! And thank you for still inviting me to fish with you, even after changing my bait a million times, untangling my line, diving into the lake to fish out my rod, and unsnagging my hook from the weeds!

When summertime comes, there's a trip that I take,
to Grandma and Grandpa, who live by a lake.

Lake Cattywampus—the name might sound strange,
but there's not a single thing here I would change.

Into his red truck goes Grandpa's canoe,
and we say to Grandma, "Be back in a few!"

AKE
ATTYWAMPUS
Then off to the lake, we go! We're on our way,
to do some canoeing and fishing today!

We put on our jackets, to keep us afloat,
in case something happens to our little boat.

But Grandpa assures me there's nothing to fear,
he's good at canoeing and knows how to steer.

To cast off the boat, Grandpa gives it a push.
He jumps in with me, and we row to the bush.

Getting there's not close; we paddle a lot,
but all the work's worth it for our favorite spot!

Grandpa tells stories and silly jokes, too, like, "I can canoe a canoe, but can you?"

I’ve never canoed a canoe on my own,
but I can help paddle one now that I’ve grown!

On Lake Cattywampus, there's so much to see,
like woodpeckers knocking up high in a tree.

And under the rocks is a small blue-tailed skink,
which scurries away just as fast as a wink!

Other small creatures come out to say, "Hi!"
They peek from the marsh as our boat passes by.

I see little brown frogs that live in the reeds.
They swim by their tadpole eggs shining like beads.

Farther up, we see a bridge made of sticks—
Grandpa says beavers are up to their tricks.

Using their front teeth, the beavers will cut branches and twigs that will make their own hut.

Reaching our spot, we are ready to fish,
I throw my rod back with a delicate swish.

I watch as my fishing line crosses the lake.
“Be careful!” says Grandpa. “Don’t make the boat shake!”

We have to be patient; but that's really fine.
And after a while, something pulls on my line!

I tug on the fishing rod, lifting it high.
I find myself staring a fish in the eye!

Leaning back proudly, I get quite a fright,
from a big snapping turtle! Be careful. They bite!

Grandpa casts his line; it’s such a good throw.
He reels in a bass from the water below.

We both have a sandwich to wrap up our day,
his is baloney, and mine's PBJ.

It’s time to go home as we near two o’clock.
We pick up our paddles and row to the dock.

Lake Cattywampus is simply the best,
but now we're both ready to have a long rest.

The End

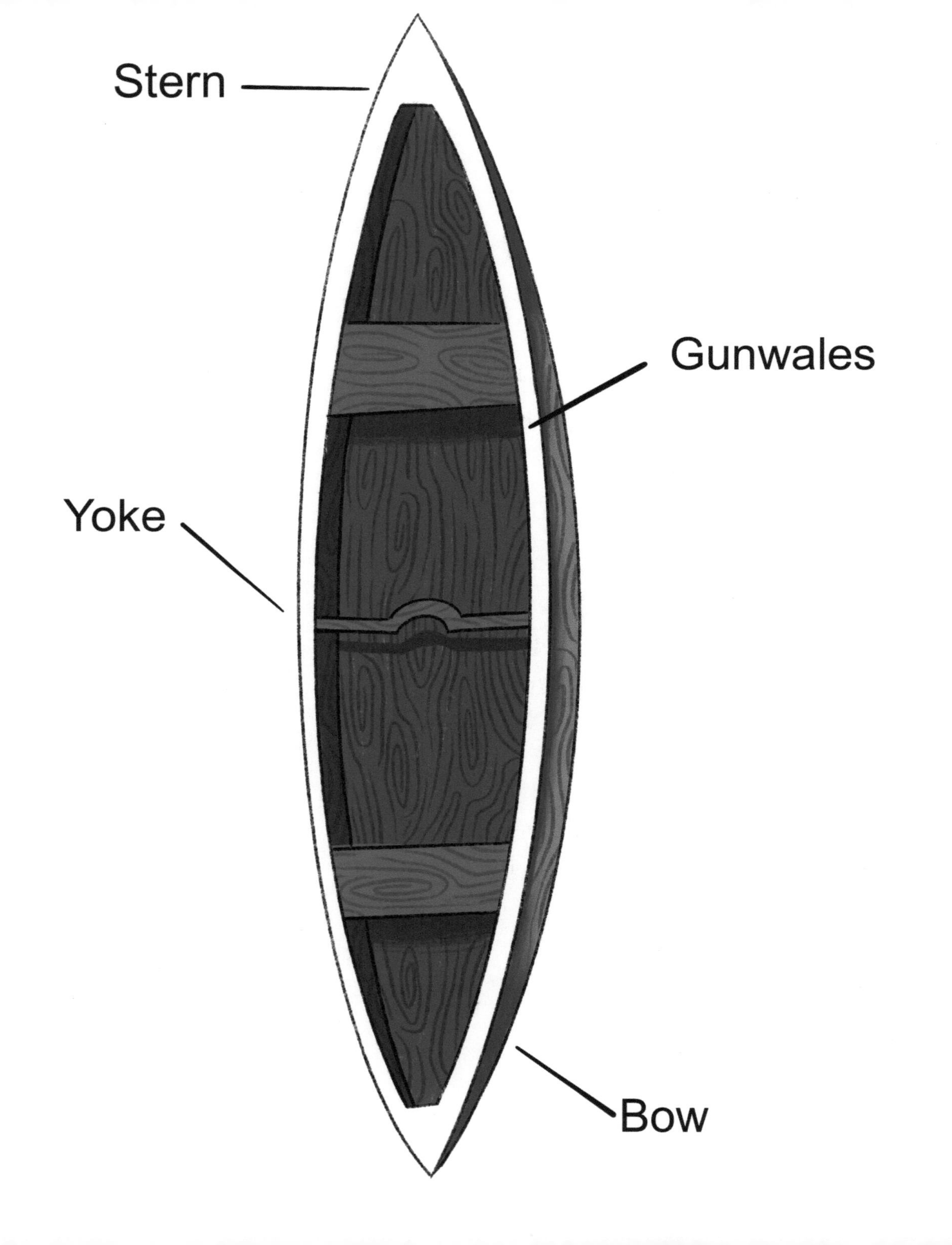
Stern
Gunwales
Yoke
Bow

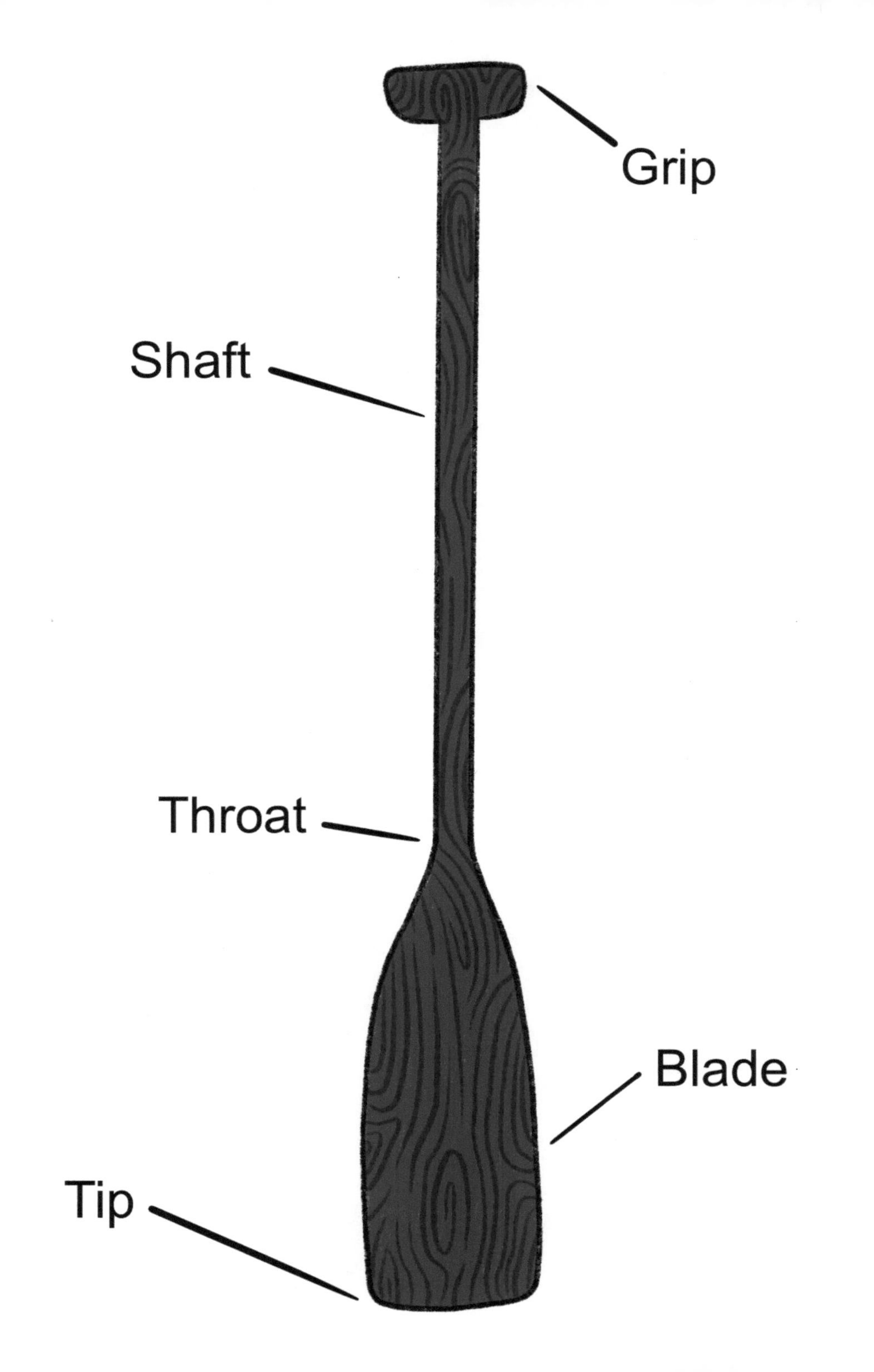
Grip
Shaft
Throat
Blade
Tip

CPSIA information can be obtained
at www.ICGtesting.com
Printed in the USA
LVHW071745210621
690773LV00006B/180

7 8 1 7 7 7 6 9 4 9 8 2 *